ZEN
and the
MAGIC
of
ROUNDABOUT
MAINTENANCE

A Brief History of Time (for Bed)

ROGER PLANER

With foreword by
NIGEL PLANER

FANTAIL

FANTAIL BOOKS

Published by the Penguin Group
Penguin Books Ltd, 27 Wrights Lane, London W8 5TZ, England
Penguin Books USA Inc., 375 Hudson Street, New York, New York 10014, USA
Penguin Books Australia Ltd, Ringwood, Victoria, Australia
Penguin Books Canada Ltd, 10 Alcorn Avenue, Toronto, Ontario, Canada M4V 3B2
Penguin Books (NZ) Ltd, 182-190 Wairau Road, Auckland 10, New Zealand

Penguin Books Ltd, Registered Offices: Harmondsworth, Middlesex, England

First published 1992
10 9 8 7 6 5 4 3 2 1

Text copyright © Roger Planer, 1992
Introduction copyright © Nigel Planer, 1992
Magic Roundabout © AB Productions SA/Serge Danot, 1992
Licensed by Link Licensing
All rights reserved

The moral right of the author has been asserted

Made and printed in Great Britain by William Clowes Limited, Beccles and London

ACKNOWLEDGEMENTS
Photographs: p.18, Sealink ferry, crates; p.42, punks; p.49, globe; p.56 & 57, house interiors (The Image Bank);
p.30, Sooty (Aquarius Picture Library); p.34, The Beatles (London Features); p.53, Scottish Terrier (Diane Pearce);
p.63, David Ike (Topham); p.30, Barbara Woodhouse (BBC Photographic Library);
p.30, Muffin the Mule (BBC/Ann Hogarth)

Illustrations: p.20/21, Dylan; p.22, Dylan and Zebedee (Bob Wagner)
Magic flowers and borders by Bob Reed

CONTENTS

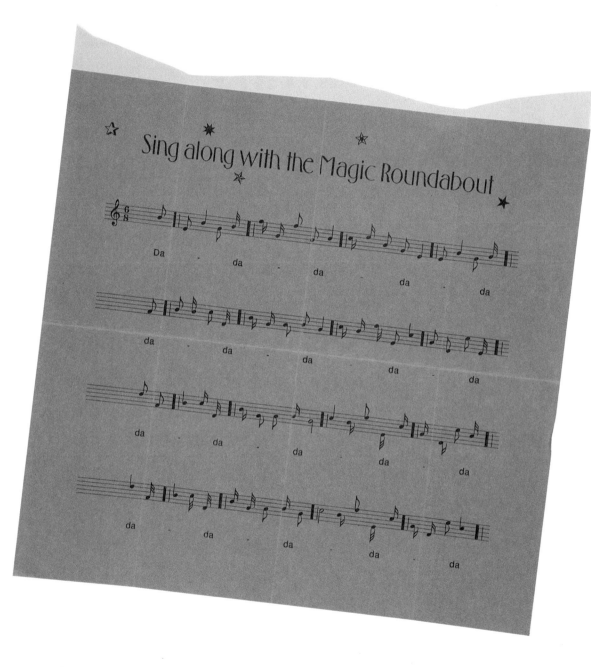

★ Amazing facts ★ — Dada is also a nihilistic European art movement.

THE MAGIC ROUNDABOUT AND HOW TO SURVIVE IT

Nigel Planer, Dorking Deprogramming and Therapeutic Clinic, May 1992

For ten years our mind-space zones and inner merry-go-rounds had been zapped by yodelling yuppies and racist rich-quicks, by loud-mouthed low-forms and second-rate sitcoms. We had been zonked in the televisuals by seedy share-sales and by tabloid tricksters. We had been packaged, poisoned and privatized, game-showed, flame-throwed and monetarized. Our jack-in-a-box factors had slouched below zero, and we had a loopy-loop rating of zilch. The profiteers had pilfered our pain parachutes while the multi-nationals made mince-meat of our magic memories . . .

And then . . . from the detritus of a dead decade emerged a video cassette. Numbed by *Neighbours*, frazzled by franchise auctions, bored by Batman and tired of anything with turtles in it, I tipped the unlabelled tape into the machine, pressed 'play' and saw . . . white noise, cloudy crackles, interference . . . nothing. I looked at the stamp on the jiffy envelope in which the video cassette had arrived. French. A video from France. With the last oodle of curiosity left in my ebbing Eighties brainscape, I twiddled the tracking

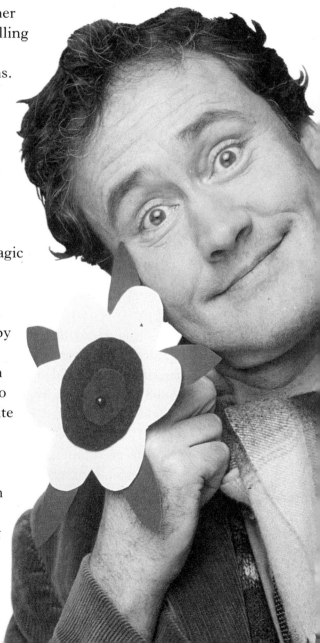

on my VHS until vague shapes stirred behind the fizzing snow on my screen. Strange noises and haunting Hammond organs lurched in and out of audio-focus, until a voice distinctly said, '*Bonjour*, Flappy,' then another, deeper, drone, '*Bonjour*, Margot.' Through the technological fog, a face, a rabbit, a snail, and then, a stupid-looking dog.

Back, back raced my mind to something lurking in the forgotten forests where I could not tell what were *my* memories, and what belonged to everyone. I adjusted my rewind facility and fast-searched the cavernous crevices of my doldrums for some trace, some imprint, of a dormant virus. I *deja*-viewed myself, for I recognized this stupid-looking dog. But how? Why? What connection did he have to the carrot-seeking cortex of my consciousness? '*Je suis Pollux, star du cinema,*' he said in French, and hid behind a cardboard tree. A decade of fruitlessness and dejection had erased the specifics, but elements were left homeopathetically crystallized on the lip of my skull from the days before thought-police, thrift and Thatcher. Tremulous, dithering, I dared to delve into the depths of my dreamtime, and dredged my decoding dials. This dog is . . . Dougal. Though what that meant, and why so dangerous was yet beyond the mobile telephone of my boom-and-bust brain.

Somewhere submerged in the swamps of my stamped-on adolescence was a Dougal, a rough-edged reminiscence, a ragged remnant of a time before the decadence, the delinquency and Docklands. Had there not been in earlier aeons, a lovingness? Before *Terminator*, a 'Time for Bed'? Before Armani and the EEC, an Ermintrude? Before Breakfast TV, a

Brian? Before flat brief-cases, famine in Africa and Channel Four, a Florence? Before *Hello!* magazine, a Hector's House?. . . But my memory-banks were becoming bloated and bedraggled, hazy, fuzzy my backward-wind facility was rusty . . . and then with one sensational synapse-leap all was savagely clear! The French video came to an end and as Mr Rusty wound his barrel organ, the theme tune thwacked me in the thorax, like tinnitus without the tin . . . this was *The Magic Roundabout*, and I must save it, or let the world for ever grovel in game-shows, Garfield and greed!

I unJeremy-Beadled myself for the task ahead. The road would be painful, unpaid and pointless. To put on *The Magic Roundabout* again – where would be the profit? Who would monopolize the merchandising? Who would take over the T-shirt franchise? Not me, that was for certain. The complete kamikazeness of my condition seemed cavalier, and consummately cranky. Could I do this crazy thing alone? No, I would need secret allies, friends in high old places, fellow freaks in subterfuge and fantasy. I faxed a film-man that I know – Brendon Donitall, the bearded baby – and conversed with him in code about this show. He had the microphones, the memory, the doughnuts and the studio. Then brother Rog, the next disciple to our Dougallish plot; he had the madness, the wordprocessor and the infuriating habit of missing every deadline, but so what? All we needed now was a broadcaster stupid enough to give us space, a silly person who wouldn't mind a bit of omelette in the face, someone with power, but who had had an egg-and-spoonful of the ratrace. Lucinda Whitenoise came along, and despite the boardroom clothes she wore, said: 'I can put you on at eight-thirty in the morning on Channel Four.' But enough, enough, of all this stupid rhyming stuff, it's time to read this tome, and if anyone can find me, please, please, send me the medicine and the bus fare so I can get home . . .

Nigel Planer

IN THE BEGINNING THERE WAS . . . ◆ ◆

It was another lovely day in the Magic Garden.
The sun was shining through the trees. Mr Rusty
was polishing the Roundabout. Dylan was
helping Mr McHenry in his greenhouse.
Ermintrude was chewing grass. No one
was in the slightest bit worried about the
single European currency or the ozone
layer. Then Dougal arrived.

'Hello, Dougal!' said Florence. 'Lovely day, isn't it?'

'Yes,' said Dougal, turning around in a circle.

'I was thinking, have you ever wondered how all of us got to be here?'
said Florence.

'Have I what?' said Dougal somewhat testily.

'You know,' said Florence. 'Ever sat down and thought, "How did I get
here?"'

Dougal looked at Florence, and thought somebody really ought to have a serious talk with her. But somehow it wasn't really his place to say anything.

'I suppose it had to happen some day,' said Dougal vaguely. 'We all go through these changes in life. Are you feeling all right?'

'Oh yes! I just sometimes wonder, you know … how it all happened,' continued Florence. 'Do you know?'

'Know? Yes, of course I know . . . I know all right! A dog doesn't get to my position in life without knowing how he got to be here,' said Dougal, looking at Florence rather coyly. 'It's just that it's not really my place to say!'

'Oh,' said Florence. 'I wonder who I should ask?'

'Want to know about the birds and the bees?' said Ermintrude, arriving. 'We cows have seen it all before, on the farmyard, you know.'

'Yes, please!' said Florence excitedly.

'That's it, just ask Aunty Ermintrude, a natural phenomenon, if ever there was!' said Dougal.

'It's all to do with "increasing the annual milk yield", you see . . .' continued Ermintrude. 'When two creatures fall in love, the farmer . . .'

'Oh, spare us the agricultural specifics, madam,' said Dougal butting in.

'I was just wondering how we got to be here,' said Florence, who was beginning to wish she'd never asked.

'Simple, I caught the bus!' said Brian.

'Oh, bravo, very good!' said Dougal. 'Straight to the point with your usual incisiveness!'

'All you need are a few pipe-cleaners, some cotton wool and a wooden ball!' said Mr McHenry, pragmatically. Florence's question was turning into a bit of a group discussion.

'Surely you don't expect her to believe that old wives' tale, do you . . .?' asked Dougal.

'Yeah, like there's a whole lot more to it. It's, like, metaphysical, man. You can get, like, reborn as yourself in exactly the same moment in time and, like, never know it happened,' said Dylan, who'd recently fallen asleep in an alternative bookshop in Glastonbury.

'Oh dear,' said Dougal.

'Oh dear,' said Florence, wishing that Zebedee would put in an appearance, but, of course, you could never tell when Zebedee would turn up.

Just then Mr Rusty finished his polishing and came over waving an oily .rag. 'You want to know how we got to be here? I'll tell you . . .' said Mr Rusty. 'I've got a story for you – a true story!'

'Oh, how exciting!' said Florence, sitting down on the grass.

'I'm literally chomping at the bit!' said Dougal, turning around in circles. Everyone else then gathered around Mr Rusty.

Suddenly they could all hear the plucking of harp strings and everything went blurred, and they knew it was time to tell a story – their own story – of how *The Magic Roundabout* began...

THE MAGIC ROUNDABOUT
FIRST TURNS

'You'd be too young to remember
France, Florence,' said Mr Rusty.
'You were called Margot then . . .
and Dougal was called Pollux.
Those were the days before the
cross-Channel ferry, before
Concorde, when most of Dylan's
brain was still working . . .'

'Wow, like prehistoric, man. Like,
many aeons ago!' said Dylan,
falling asleep.

'We all lived in gay Parée. . .' continued Mr Rusty.

'Oh *magnifique*!' said Florence.

'I was an organ-grinder on the Champs-Elysées at the time!' mused Mr
Rusty.

'I was a well-known figure in café society,' said Dougal. 'Used to hang
around with Jean-Paul Sartre and his brother Gaultier, you know, just
for laughs.'

'Sounds jolly bohemian!' said Ermintrude.

'Then one day, I came across an oddly shaped parcel with a note on it,'
said Mr Rusty.

'Called but you were out. Please find enclosed one Magic Roundabout.
Order number 34343. Regards Zebedee.'

'Inside I found a book of instructions, I read them and re-read them and re-read them, because they kept changing before my eyes... but eventually I managed to put it together with the help of my friend Serge Danot.

MAGIC ROUNDABOUT MODEL X2232

Instructions for Assembly

If assembled and maintained correctly this roundabout should be able to perform the following improbable tasks.

- Going backwards in time.

- Fixing the weather.

- Make most objects speak (except heavy stoneware)

- Dogs chirp.

- Birds Bark.

- Transmute matter into anything (liquid not recommended).

IMPORTANT

Improbable tasks ONLY.

This is a MAGIC Roundabout and is not recommended for normal use.

Keep away from curses etc...

Magic R

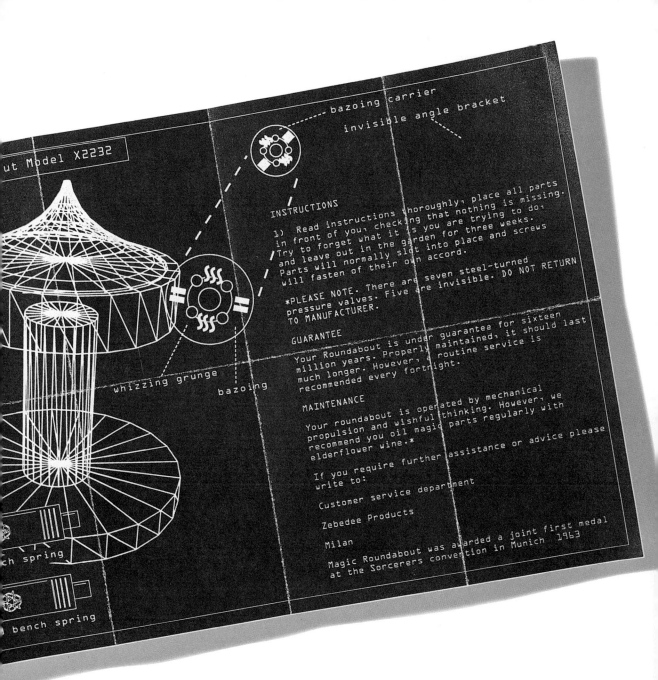

ut Model X2232

bazoing carrier

invisible angle bracket

whizzing grunge

bazoing

ch spring

bench spring

INSTRUCTIONS

1) Read instructions thoroughly, place all parts in front of you, checking that nothing is missing. Try to forget what it is you are trying to do, and leave out in the garden for three weeks. Parts will normally slot into place and screws will fasten of their own accord.

*PLEASE NOTE. There are seven steel-turned pressure valves. Five are invisible. DO NOT RETURN TO MANUFACTURER.

GUARANTEE

Your Roundabout is under guarantee for sixteen million years. Properly maintained, it should last much longer. However, a routine service is recommended every fortnight.

MAINTENANCE

Your roundabout is operated by mechanical propulsion and wishful thinking. However, we recommend you oil magic parts regularly with elderflower wine.*

If you require further assistance or advice please write to:

Customer service department

Zebedee Products

Milan

Magic Roundabout was awarded a joint first medal at the Sorcerers convention in Munich 1963

* Elderflower wine was very popular in the Sixties, though no self-respecting Frenchman would dream of drinking it. It is, however, excellent for oiling magic parts of the Roundabout and improving particularly poor quality home brew. One of the suspected reasons for the success of the Magic Roundabout in England is the abundance of it at the time. No pine-clad 'semi' was without a fermenting bottle of Elderflower in the shed which would be brought out by a crazed town planner who'd found it was the cheapest way of poisoning his dinner guests.

'There was always something special about it, something magical!' said Mr Rusty. 'I knew that the moment I set eyes on it. First there was you, and the others who came to ride on it, Florence. Then the animals, then the TV people, then came the existentialists. Oh, how I hated the existentialists, always after a free ride.'

'What's an existentialist?' asked Florence.

'Oh, it's a Frenchman who likes elderflower wine, Florence. Not many of them about now, but Paris was crawling with them in those days.'

'O innocent youth! O sweet memories of childhood!' said Dougal, nostalgically shedding a tear. 'Long summer days in the garden.'

'Yes, they were happy days indeed,' said Mr Rusty.
'Then one day along came Brian.'

'Oh woe . . . o loss of innocence!' said Dougal, spinning round and round. 'A snail has crept into our garden paradise bearing strange and unwanted fruit!'

'Hello,' said Brian, sidling up to Dougal, just as he had all those many years ago.

'Can't you think of a more original way of introducing yourself, you measly mollusc?' said Dougal.

'Well, I've tried a few other things like "Greetings" and "Howdee" but "Hello" just seems to be more "me",' said Brian. 'It's my catch-phrase.'

'Pathetic!' said Dougal.

'Do you have a better suggestion?' asked Brian.

'How about "I'm just about to leave"?' said Dougal. 'That trips off the tongue rather easily!'

'Oh, Dougal, you are a card!' said Brian.

'That's just how it always was between them,' said Mr Rusty. 'Naked hostility.'

'Yes, Dougal,' said Florence. 'You always were a bit rude to Brian!'

'Rude? Me? On the contrary, I have always behaved with the utmost decorum and respect for my little shell-based companion!' objected Dougal.

'Yes, well, that isn't quite how I remember it!' said Mr Rusty. He turned the handle of the Magic Roundabout backwards in time to one sunny day in the distant past when Dougal decided to form a golf club. He gathered all the others together for his inaugural speech . . .

DOUGAL: And so without further ado . . . it falls to me, as president of this golf club, to preside over the aforementioned golf club, which I will do, without further ado . . . Any questions?

BRIAN: Yes. Why do we have to have a golf club in the first place?

DOUGAL: Ehem, yes, I was coming to that. The reason we have a golf club is – so that we can refuse to let some people join it.

BRIAN: But that's not fair.

DOUGAL: Well, we can't just let anyone in you know, otherwise what would be the point? Now if there are no more questions I would like to move on to discuss rules concerning membership . . . ehem.

ERMINTRUDE: I might not want to join anyway.

DOUGAL: Rule No One. You have to be a personal friend of Bruce Forsyth or Jimmy Tarbuck. Rule No Two. You have to wear a pair of checked trousers and a v-neck sweater. Rule No Three. Donate a minimum of three pounds of sugar to the club treasury every week. Rule No Four. Satisfy the board of examiners that you are not a snail.

BRIAN: You can't say that! It's snailist.

DOUGAL: Well, we can't have snails on the golf course, crawling all over the place ruining the grass. Go on, shoo, shoo off with you, go bury yourself in a bunker!

'Yes,' said Dougal, when the Magic Roundabout had stopped turning. 'I suppose I have on occasion had to be quite firm with the little crustacean!'

'Oh, Dougal, Brian has always been perfectly nice and you've always been perfectly horrible to him!' said Florence.

'Yes, quite!' said Brian.

'Correction,' said Dougal. 'A snail cannot possibly be perfectly nice, it's a contradiction in terms.'

'What do you mean by that?' said Brian, boldly.

'Because he is a snail – and therefore "snailful". Anything that is snailful is, by definition, perfectly horrible. Something can only be perfectly nice if it is "snailfree", thus, words like "sun", "tree" and "sugar". However "crawl" and "nasty, wriggly thing on the ground" are snailful and are therefore horrible. Hence the expressions: "This milk is off – it smells snaily", "it was a snailful film last night" and "your timing was snailable." It's in the dictionary.'

'Oh yes, written by who?' said Brian, who was now beginning to get a little peeved.

'Someone very wise and very close to my heart!' said Dougal, looking self-important.

'You, in other words,' said Brian.

'Exactly,' said Dougal. 'Now where was I?'

'You were just saying how you've always been perfectly nice to Brian,' said Florence helpfully.

'Oh yes,' said Dougal. 'So I was. But I've always been perfectly reasonable to simple-celled organisms.' Dougal looked round at the faces of the others for reassurance.

'I've always been reasonably nice to Brian, considering he's a snail,' revised Dougal. 'Besides I've always been exceptionally nice to everyone else. Haven't I?' There was a long silence, while everyone seemed to become very thoughtful.

'Then let's see, shall we?' said Mr Rusty, who was trying to say something supportive. Heaving a rather heavy sigh, he turned the Magic Roundabout handle back to the day they all packed their bags and set sail for England.

ABOARD THE CROSS-CHANNEL FERRY

DOUGAL: Ah, England, this England! Ah, this sceptred jewel in an emerald isle!

Dougal was looking out to sea on the deck of the cross-Channel ferry.

DOUGAL: Nation of dog lovers! Pet fanciers. The province of the pampered pooch. Yes, I think we shall do very well in England, very well indeed!

BRIAN: At least I won't end up on your dinner plate!

Brian was quite glad to be leaving France.

DOUGAL: Fear not, mollusc. You will not be going anywhere near my plate if I've got anything to do with it! I shall have breakfast at Claridges, tea at Fortnums and dinner at the Savoy.

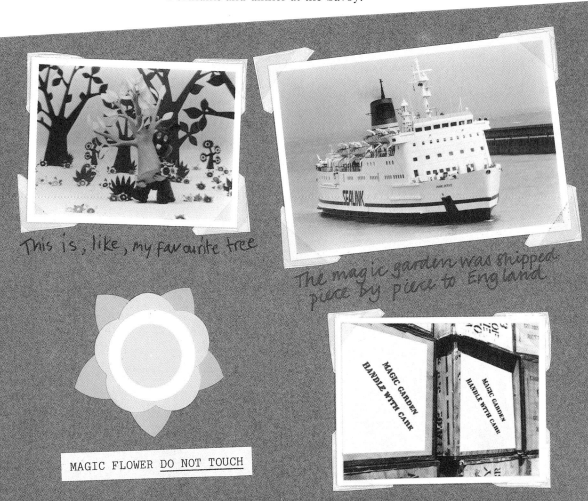

This is, like, my favourite tree

The magic garden was shipped piece by piece to England

MAGIC FLOWER DO NOT TOUCH

MAGIC GARDEN HANDLE WITH CARE

MAGIC GARDEN HANDLE WITH CARE

And Dougal had a little dream that he was sitting in an expensive restaurant peeping out from under the coat of a very rich woman who was feeding him sugar.

MR RUSTY: I just hope the Roundabout will be all right, I hate to think of it all stacked up in those crates.

ERMINTRUDE: I still don't see why we had to leave France.

DOUGAL: We are setting sail for pastures new. To England's green and pleasant land. And you, ungrateful quadruped, will have the chance to munch your way right through it.

FLORENCE: Hello, isn't it a lovely day!

For it was always a lovely day in the Magic Garden. Or if it wasn't a lovely day it was a lovely night. Florence had never been on a cross-Channel ferry before and didn't really know how to say, 'This is one of the most unpleasant experiences of my life and I think I'm going to be violently ill.'

ERMINTRUDE: Are you feeling quite well, Florence?

FLORENCE: Shall we go to the garden?

DOUGAL: My lady, let me escort you to a resting place, where you may perchance recover.

Florence was swaying on her feet.

DYLAN: Wow, I just had, like, a mind-blowing experience!

Dylan emerged from a broom cupboard.

DYLAN: I was, like, sleeping, and all of a sudden I felt the boat, like, get up and start walking to England, and I thought, like, wow, sailing is amazing because you're, like horizontal all the time, even when you're, like, walking around, and then I heard this amazing music, like someone banging a tin bath inside my head, and then I realized that what I'm feeling is, like, seasick and it's, like, a really far-out experience.

Dylan walked hastily to the side of the boat.

FLORENCE: Oh dear!

Florence was looking rather blue.

The 'amazing music' that Dylan had heard was in fact a group of students with a guitar singing 'Stairway to Heaven', while sitting cross-legged on the sundeck. To understand why Dylan found this and travelling on a cross-Channel ferry a 'mindblowing experience' we have to understand more about the workings of his brain, which have confounded psychologists and neurologists alike.

Its structure is, in fact, unique in the biological world, most closely resembling the organic composition and evolution of a turnip.

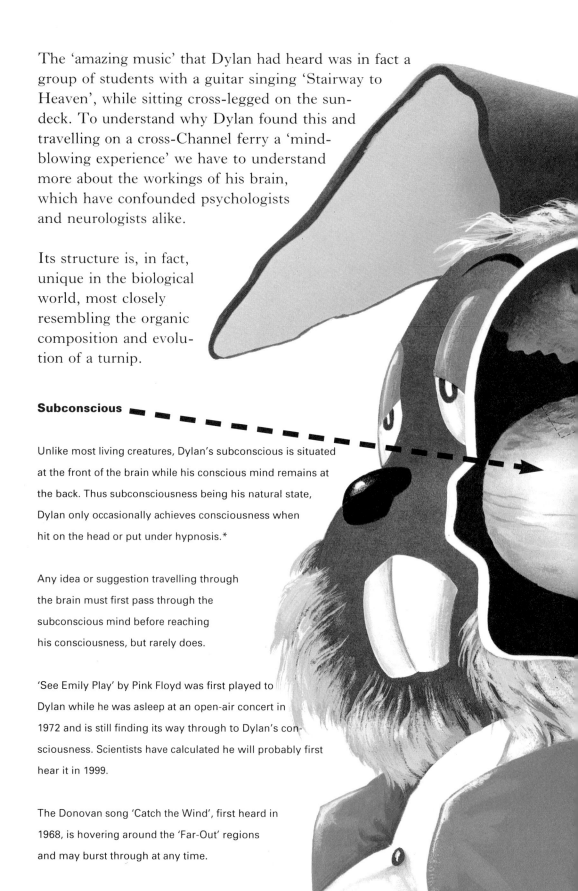

Subconscious

Unlike most living creatures, Dylan's subconscious is situated at the front of the brain while his conscious mind remains at the back. Thus subconsciousness being his natural state, Dylan only occasionally achieves consciousness when hit on the head or put under hypnosis.*

Any idea or suggestion travelling through the brain must first pass through the subconscious mind before reaching his consciousness, but rarely does.

'See Emily Play' by Pink Floyd was first played to Dylan while he was asleep at an open-air concert in 1972 and is still finding its way through to Dylan's consciousness. Scientists have calculated he will probably first hear it in 1999.

The Donovan song 'Catch the Wind', first heard in 1968, is hovering around the 'Far-Out' regions and may burst through at any time.

The Wilderness

'Fire Brigade' by Move is almost certainly lost in Dylan's subconscious and it is now unlikely he will ever hear it.

Memory

Now largely unused, Dylan's memory was last emptied in 1986 and was found to contain only one Jimi Hendrix riff and half a verse of 'Whiter Shade of Pale'.

The Far-Out Regions

The 'Far-Out' regions of Dylan's brain are conversely situated near the front of the conscious mind. Thus any idea or stimulus making it through to the conscious mind is sure to acquire the status of 'far-outness', however banal.

Critical faculties

The critical faculties are situated in such a remote part of Dylan's subconscious that most stimuli never bother to go there and bypass them altogether, hence the reference to the amazing music in 'Stairway to Heaven'.

Speech Centre

Dylan's distinctive vocabulary has long been the subject of debate and analysis amongst sociologists. Some attribute its high–density use of Californian phrases such as 'Far Out' to a genetically replicated experience inherited via an American ancestor. Others have speculated about a 'big bang' – one central experience, which has generated a number of phrases and words, which are still being assimilated. It is also important to note that phrases leaving this part of the brain

*There is also a scientific phenomenon known as 'Dylan Speed'. This represents the average length of time it takes an unobstructed thought to pass from Dylan's subconscious into his conscious mind – ten years. It is certainly impossible for this process to take place within the same decade.

automatically have the word 'man' attached to them, resulting in some interesting confusions.

For example, the following conversation which Dylan once had with Zebedee during breakfast:

'Can you pass the milk, man?'
said Dylan.

'Certainly,' said Zebedee.

'No, man, that's the milkman, man'

'No, this is the milkmanman.'
said Zebedee.

'No, man, not the guy who
delivers it to the door, man.'

'What's the doorman
got to do with it?'

DOUGAL: O England, merry old England. This England! This green and pleasant land.

Dougal sniffed the air as they walked off the boat.

DOUGAL: Home of my ancestors!

BRIAN: I thought they were French aristrocrats!

DOUGAL: We were an extended family. Ah, Britannia. It smells of muffins and sugar bread. Yes, a dog like me could feel at home in England.

Suddenly a man appeared.

ERIC: Are you the Magic Roundabout.

It was Eric Thompson, who'd come to take charge of everything in England.

DOUGAL: Pardon? *Qu'est que c'est?*

Dougal pretended not to be able to speak English.

ERIC: The Magic Roundabout? *Le Menage Enchanté?*

DOUGAL: Oh, no, no . . . you've got completely the wrong idea, sir, we are a group of German diplomats returning from a convention in Berne. Who do you think we are?

BRIAN: Steady on!

DOUGAL: How many three-inch snails with stupid hats do you see alighting from this ferry? How many?

ERIC: I'm afraid the customs officers want to see Dougal.

DOUGAL: What, me?

DYLAN: Oh no, like, heavy!

It was true. The customs officers did want to see Dougal, and they led him away to a little room.

DOUGAL: Unhand me, you oaf, how dare you?

FLORENCE: Oh dear . . . what are they doing with Dougal?

ERIC: They're putting him in quarantine.

Florence wondered to herself what 'quarantine' was and whether she could join in, then hearing Dougal protesting from behind the door, decided it probably wasn't much fun.

DOUGAL: Rabies! Rabies! I've never bitten anyone in my life. Mind you, there's always the first time!

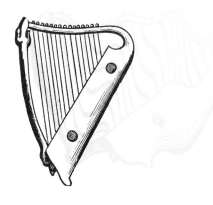

ZEBEDEE'S DEAL WITH THE BBC

'Let's bounce a few ideas across the table, run it up the flagpole and jump into bed with it.'

'Hello,' said Zebedee, bouncing in on schedule.

'I was wondering when you were going to show up,' said Dougal.

'Thought I better make an appearance,' said Zebedee. 'Make sure you get the facts straight, could be tricky, legally, you know, telling the Magic Roundabout story. Now, where are you up to?'

'The bit where you come in,' said Mr Rusty.

'Ah yes,' said Zebedee, taking up the story. 'Of course, while you lot were on the ferry, I was hopping backwards and forwards between England and France, sorting out contracts with the BBC. Very particular they were at the BBC – wanted to make sure we set a good example to their viewers.'

'What does "a good example" mean?' said Florence. Zebedee twitched his moustache and signalled to Mr Rusty to turn back the magic handle.

'That's what they said "in writing",' said Zebedee, magicking up a letter from the BBC.

'Frankly, I couldn't have agreed more,' said Dougal, nodding. 'The rest of you were simply not being nice enough to me. I'd known it for some time. I even put in a few story suggestions of my own, if I remember. Let me think now, yes, *'Everyone buys Dougal a present, Dougal gets lots of sugar for being good, Brian apologizes for being a snail'*!

Children's **B B C**

Childrens Television,
Television Centre,
BBC Wood Lane,
London.

Dear Mr Zebedee,

Re The Magic Roundabout.

Here at the BBC we are anxious that our programmes should reflect the example of good neighbourliness and courtesy, set by previous luminaries, Muffin the Mule, Bill and Ben, and Andy Pandy.

While we find your idea for 'the adventures of a little girl and her faithful little dog' quite promising, we would like to advise on certain matters of BBC policy which, coming from France you may not be familiar with.

NODDING

We are particularly keen that characters should nod whenever possible - denoting as it does, an agreeable nature and a willing disposition. We feel that a great deal of nodding is essential for the character formation of young children.

RAILLERY

Excessive railing and 'calling of names' is not encouraged, particularly between dumb animals such as dogs, snails and cows. Characters should at all times be tolerant, helpful and nod frequently.

Please find enclosed a suggested storyline you may like to consider.

```
DOUGAL      Hello, Florence.

Dougal nodded.

FLORENCE    Hello, Dougal.

Florence nodded.

DOUGAL      What are you doing, Florence?

FLORENCE    I'm helping Mr Rusty, who's old, by doing the
            washing-up.

said Florence still nodding.

DOUGAL      How considerate you are, Florence. May I help?

FLORENCE    Oh, no(more nodding), for you are a dog, and
            only girls can do the washing-up!

ERMINTRUDE  She's right, only girls can do the washing-up.
            May I help?

FLORENCE    Oh, thank you, Ermintrude. You're very helpful.

BRIAN       Yes, you are both very helpful. Very helpful indeed!

Everyone agreed that Florence and Ermintrude were both very
helpful indeed and they all nodded a lot until Zebedee arrived.

ZEBEDEE     Time to help Mr Rusty stack the dishes.

Zebedee nodded.

END


Hope this is helpful ...

Yours sincerely,
```

'Apparently what they wanted from you
was a touch of gentility and respectfulness to raise
the tone a bit,' said Mr McHenry.

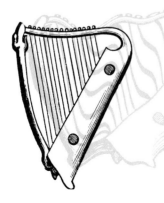

'Exactly. And was I not respectful
and gentle?' said Dougal, as Mr
Rusty turned back the magic handle
once again.

DOUGAL: Ah, Brian, may I have a word in 'your shell-like'?

BRIAN: Certainly, Dougal, me old chum . . .

DOUGAL: It's about Ermintrude, doesn't she make you sick?

BRIAN: What, old Ermi?

DOUGAL: Sshh, I don't want anyone to hear this, but have you noticed she looks like a barrage balloon on stilts?

BRIAN: What do you mean?

DOUGAL: As in great big inflatable thing with funny legs – a barrage balloon on stilts

ERMINTRUDE: A barrage balloon on stilts?

Ermintrude was eavesdropping from behind a tree. Just then Florence arrived.

DOUGAL: Sssh, here comes Florence!

FLORENCE: Hello there, has anyone seen Ermintrude?

DOUGAL: It's hard to miss her usually, isn't it?

FLORENCE: I haven't seen her for ages!

DOUGAL: Might give the garden a chance to grow again . . . heh heh.

BRIAN: Dougal just called her a barrage balloon on stilts!

DOUGAL: Tell-tale!

FLORENCE: You ought not to talk behind her back, you know, Dougal.

DOUGAL: Which bit of her would you prefer me to talk behind?

FLORENCE: If you've got anything to say, you should say it straight to her face.

DOUGAL: You're right. Now, where is she? Ermintrude! O corpulent one, I've something to tell you.

That wasn't quite what they were after was it?' said Zebedee. 'The BBC were most upset, not enough nodding, they said. We even received letters from pressure groups.'

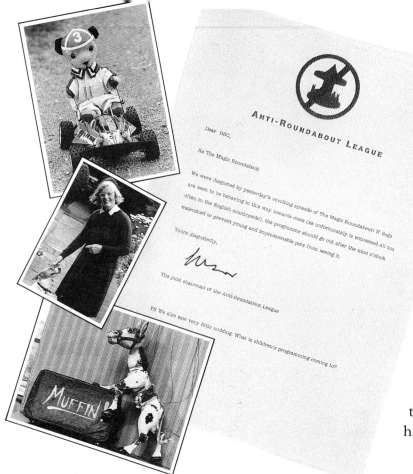

ANTI-ROUNDABOUT LEAGUE

Dear BBC,

Re The Magic Roundabout

We were disgusted by yesterday's revolting episode of The Magic Roundabout! If dogs are seen to be behaving in this way towards cows (as unfortunately is witnessed all too often in the English countryside), the programme should go out after the nine o'clock watershed to prevent young and impressionable pets from seeing it.

Yours disgustedly,

The joint chairman of the Anti-Roundabout League

PS We also saw very little nodding. What is children's programming coming to?

'If I have ever been anything less than one hundred per cent complimentary about Ermintrude, it has been for her own good,' said Dougal, roughly grabbing the handle from Mr Rusty and turning it anti-clockwise.

'What about the time she went to the hairdresser and I bought her a Mexican hat to cover up that awful hairdo?' said Dougal.

'What a selfless gesture that was!' said Brian.

'Or the time I extracted one of her teeth with my very own dental invention!' Dougal added.

'Stand aside, Mother Theresa,' said Brian.

'Things went from bad to worse,' said Zebedee.

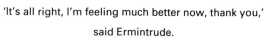

'It's all right, I'm feeling much better now, thank you,' said Ermintrude.

'There was the time Dougal pushed Brian down an ink-well to see how deep it was!' said Mr Rusty.

'The day he tried to sell me to a snail farm,' said Brian indignantly.

'Not to mention the day he took Ermintrude to the market and tried to swap her for a bag of barley sugar!' said Zebedee.

Dougal felt that everyone was being a little unfair to him and he decided to position himself behind a bush until everyone stopped.

'The straw that broke the camel's back happened the next day, when Ermintrude had her little conversation with the train!' said Mr Rusty.

'It was a very emotional time for me!' said Ermintrude, as Mr Rusty spun the Magic Roundabout back in time to the fateful day that Ermintrude tried to end it all.

ERMINTRUDE: Oh . . . oh, life is too awful!

Ermintrude walked down the tracks in front of the train.

DOUGAL: Get out the way at once, Ermintrude, you great lumbering milk-float!

Dougal was shouting from the cabin.

TRAIN: We apologize to passengers for the delay. We ask you all to remain seated.

ERMINTRUDE: Why don't you just run me over. Nobody wants me. They're better off without me, so why don't you just run me down. After all, what's a little less butter on the EEC butter mountain matter to anyone.

The train looked at Ermintrude and decided it was probably better to take the softly, softly approach under the circumstances.

TRAIN: I'd really rather not, if it's all the same to you.

ERMINTRUDE: You'd rather not? Oh, how sweet of you.

Ermintrude was secretly a little chuffed.

ERMINTRUDE: You know, most trains wouldn't be nearly so sympathetic, they'd run you over soon as look at you. Trains can be so mechanical sometimes, don't you think? But you're not like that at all. Have you ever thought of settling down to graze somewhere, in a field? I hear Hertfordshire is nice.

DOUGAL: Are you going to get out of the way or are we going to have to mow you down, you great inflatable oil tanker!

'Everyone said that Dougal had driven her to despair with his "incessant taunting",' said Zebedee, when the Magic Roundabout had stopped moving.

'It does look a bit like it, Dougal,' said Florence.

'It was a stunt! She's a fraud! She's always faking something, the great theatrical ham!' said Dougal.

B.N.C.A.

Dear sir,

I was disgusted by Dougal's behaviour in yesterday's Magic Roundabout episode portraying Ermintrude and the train. I consider it very important to engender a positive attitude towards cows even if they are a bit lumpy and stupid. We demand an apology.

Yours sincerely,

The Be Nicer to Cows Association

'It did wonders for the ratings, dear heart,' said Ermintrude.

'Unsuitable for children's viewing, Dougal's the villain of the piece,' said Mr Rusty. 'The letters came in thick and fast.'

'The BBC demanded we make an official apology "to cows in all fields of life"!' said Zebedee.

'We challenged Dougal to say five nice things about Ermintrude, I bet he couldn't do it!' said Brian.

'You had such little faith in my creative ability,' said Dougal, as Mr Rusty wound the magic handle back to Dougal's written apology to Ermintrude.

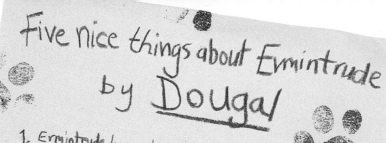

Five nice things about Ermintrude by Dougal

1. Ermintrude has got nice teeth

Ermintrude has enviable teeth. They shine out, illuminating and radiant promontories, lighthouses in a troubled sea, guiding wayward sailors to safety. The excellence of her teeth are highlighted by the considerable deficiencies in other areas like the brain. Ermintrude's brain is such a small, ill-conceived and ultimately mistaken organ in comparison to her teeth which shine like beacons of light in the darkness.

2. Ermintrude has not started any world wars

As far as can be realistically ascertained Ermintrude has not started any wars, oppressed any minorities, plotted, imprisoned, conspired bribed or extorted anybody in anyway whatsoever. It is, in fact, difficult to imagine how she could do so on account of the size and capacity of her brain which is very small indeed.

3. Ermintrude chews grass.

Though on the surface this might seem a useless and mindless activity, and something that only a lumbering pea-brained gro-bag would find interesting, it does have some useful consequences — namely making Ermintrude no threat to the dwindling world supplies of sugar.

4. There is only one Ermintrude

Ermintrude is, as far as I know completely unique. There are no cows of exactly the same stature, markings, temperament, metabolism, dental formation, or who have such negligible mental capacity. It is indeed hard to underestimate the negligibleness of her mental capacity. Of this we can be thankful. For it is worrying to imagine what an animal would do with all that bulk if it had an ounce of grey matter between its ears.

'There,' said Dougal.

'We asked for five nice things about Ermintrude, that's only four,' said Brian.

'What more do you want, blood?'

'Thank you, Dougal,' said Ermintrude. 'Four nice things was perfectly sufficient. It's the thought that counts!'

'Time to move on!' said Zebedee.

PEACE, LOVE AND MERCHANDISING

'Remember the swinging Sixties,' said Zebedee. 'A time when anything was possible; you could do your own thing, or even somebody else's thing if you wanted to.'

'Oh yes, the Roundabout was in full swing in those days,' said Mr Rusty. 'Firing out magic in all directions; talking doors, shooting stars, dancing bottles. No one could get it running like Eric, of course. He had the knack.'

'It's a wonder they didn't take the progamme off,' said Mr McHenry.

'The funny thing was, the wilder things got the more popular we became. The BBC were furious!' said Mr Rusty.

'And before we knew it we were all famous!' said Zebedee.

'In my case, it was only a matter of time,' said Dougal.

'We were household names!' said Brian excitedly.

'Ah yes, I remember the Sixties,' said Dougal. 'The nightclubs, the flashing cameras, wild nights at the Chelsea Arts Club, dear Bianca!' And he disappeared to the back of the garden.

'Wow,' said Dylan, 'the Sixties was like the high point of my whole career, and I, like, slept right through it!'

'But didn't you get to meet those lovely boys, the Beatles?' said Ermintrude, 'whilst I opened school fêtes.'

'They made me an honorary member of the Magic Circle,' said Mr Rusty.

'And I looked after the merchandising,' said Zebedee.

'I made a guest appearance on the *Andy Williams Show*,' said Brian.

'I went to bed at five forty-five when Zebedee told us to. I thought everyone did?' said Florence, who was learning a lot of new things today.

'And then came the film – I sometimes wish they'd never asked Dougal to do it,' said Mr Rusty.

'*Dougal and the Blue Cat* it was called, or *Dougal* as he preferred it to be known,' said Zebedee.

'The glare of attention was just too much for him,' said Mr Rusty. 'The lights, the cameras.'

'He wouldn't speak to us any more,' said Ermintrude. 'If you said anything at all to him he'd just say, "I'll have to speak to my agent."'

'Even if his agent asked him something he'd say, "I'll have to speak to my agent,"' said Brian.

'He was convinced he was Hollywood-bound,' said Mr McHenry.

'So I was, if it hadn't been for some unfortunate circumstances,' said Dougal, who had just returned from the back of the garden.

And Mr Rusty wound the magic handle back once more to the day that Dougal decided to have a party for all his 'showbiz' friends.

★ ★ ★ ★ ★ ★ ★ ★
DOUGAL'S HOLLYWOOD PARTY
★ ★ ★ ★ ★ ★ ★ ★

DOUGAL: What I should do, is have a party, a Hollywood party on the lawn to celebrate my brilliant new career as a film star! Yes, now let me think – a modest affair, I think, with a large white marble staircase and a hundred waiters on roller skates serving cocktails. Now, how shall I make my entrance?

And Dougal rehearsed a few steps down an imaginary staircase, first on the right, then on the left, wondering which side did the most justice to his profile.

DOUGAL: Of course, I'll have to get wardrobe to knock me up something for the occasion . . . perhaps a little off-the-shoulder toga . . . yes, that would be nice and I ought to have a wig designer . . . even if I don't have a wig! . . . Now . . . what about these cocktails.

Walking up to the Roundabout, Dougal found a large barrel of elderflower wine Mr Rusty and Eric had been using to oil the Roundabout.

DOUGAL: Hmm ... what's this? 'Elderflower wine'. I wonder if anyone would mind if I used a little of this for the cocktails, just to get it started.

Dougal sniffed the barrel a little cautiously then rolled it over a few times and took a little sip.

DOUGAL: Ughh! Not enough sugar! We'll soon see to that.

And Dougal put a few sugar-lumps into the barrel to sweeten it up a bit.

DOUGAL: Now what else shall I put in? Perhaps a few flowers . . . some younger flowers . . . How's that? . . . Yeeuch!

And Dougal put some more sugar into the barrel to cover up the taste of the younger flowers.

DOUGAL: Now shall I invite – Harold Wilson perhaps? Sophia Loren? No, she probably already has a dog. Or seven! I couldn't have that . . . I'm a one-woman dog. Now, what about Zsa Zsa Gabor? Or Elizabeth Taylor? Yes, I'll ask Liz, I'm sure she'll jump at the chance, and I'll get my mate Davy Bailey to take the photographs.

And Dougal picked a few leaves and put them in his Hollywood cocktail, and then some more sugar just for good measure.

DOUGAL: That should do the trick . . . Now I suppose I ought to ask Florence . . . ?
But then again she'll want to bring that wretched menagerie of
farmyard animals with her. Perhaps I'd better not tell her about it –
might cramp my style. And anyway I only want sophisticated socialites
at my party . . . like . . . Andy Warhol! Yes, I must ask him. I'm sure
he's longing to meet me!

*And Dougal poured a few cans of tinned soup into his cocktail, tasted it and put in some
more sugar.*

DOUGAL: Yes, sophisticated showbiz acolytes, to celebrate a star in the making . . .
I shall ask Andy Warhol, Elizabeth Taylor, Tommy Steele, and Pluto
because he might be able to give me a few Hollywood tips. Yes, that
should be a good social mix, I can see it now!

*Dougal stirred the cocktails and suddenly felt rather tired. He put in some old wood
shavings, a lot more sugar, took a sip and started to dream about his Hollywood party.*

DOUGAL'S DREAM

Everyone was there, all Dougal's new showbusiness friends, and they all wanted to speak to him.

Andy, so pleased you could make it, yes I've always loved your work too . . . famous for fifteen minutes? Four minutes and twenty seconds actually, every day just before the news. What? You'd like to paint my portrait? Oh well, I'll have to see if I can find the time. You only need a photograph? Oh well, naturally, anything for art, Andy, have you met Pluto? Yes, Pluto, is a great friend of Liz, no, I haven't been ignoring you, Liz, I promise. What's that, Liz? Congratulations? Oh, thank you, you enjoyed the film? You don't mean the film. What then? An Oscar? . . . I haven't won an Oscar, have I? No? A royal visit? Tonight? From the Queen? I'm to become 'Sir Dougal!'? The Queen's right-hand dog! 'The Order of the Royal Corgis!'?

Dougal woke up with a start, and immediately spun round in a few token circles.

DOUGAL: Good gracious! The Queen's coming here tonight! I'm not ready. Make-up, lights! What about a speech, I must have a speech. Your Royal Highness, I magnificently accept this humble honour. No, no, no! Now which knee shall I bend?

Dougal spun round a few more times and then remembered it had only been a dream.

DOUGAL: Oh, thank goodness. It was only a dream. I dreamt the whole thing! A mere fancy. Oh dear, oh dear. But then again, it might have been a premonition. Perhaps the Queen really is coming tonight and she just popped into my dream to warn me! I shouldn't be at all surprised, it's the sort of thing they do, you know, royalty. I've sensed a royal visit was in the air for some time. Help, what shall I do? What shall I wear?

And Dougal raced up to the Magic Roundabout for inspiration and then had an idea of his own . . .

DOUGAL: If only I could be sure she really was coming tonight? There must be a way to find out.

Dougal had often seen Mr Rusty turning the handle backwards to summon up the past, and wondered now, if he turned the handle fast-forward if he might not be able to summon up the future. Stepping up to the handle he gave it a brief nudge in an experimental sort of way. Then he pushed it with all his strength, but the handle refused to budge.

DOUGAL: Pathetic piece of cowboy plumbing. Doesn't it realize, I'm on royal business!

Abandoning the handle, Dougal lifted the barrel filled with his Hollywood cocktail on to the Magic Roundabout, jumped up himself, and emptied the whole thing into the inner workings of the machine.

DOUGAL: That should do the trick! Confounded spinning-top!

The elder flowers and the younger flowers, the leaves, the tinned soup, the wood shavings and all that sugar seeped into the machinery and the Magic Roundabout began to move. Slowly at first, as Dougal jumped on to a horse and started to cheer, then faster and faster as Dougal whooped and his hair stood on end, then whizzing round, at hundreds of miles an hour, as Dougal hung on for dear life and yelped for it to stop. But on it went, spinning off its axis and flying through the air, skimming the flowers and scorching the trees of the Magic Garden until finally Dougal could hang on no longer, went flying through the air and landed in a tree – a miserable, frightened and rather windswept little dog.

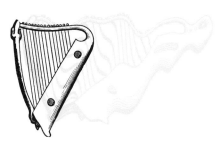

THE WILDERNESS YEARS

'The Roundabout was ruined,' said Mr Rusty.

'And, of course, without the Roundabout there was no programme,' said Zebedee.

'Or Magic Garden,' said Mr McHenry.

'No school fêtes to open, no Donny Osmond,' said Ermintrude.

Dougal suddenly became very busy coughing behind a tree.

'Instead it was *Hector's House*,' said Brian.

'Punk music, the Falklands, and Ninja turtles,' said Zebedee.

'We all had to fend for ourselves in the outside world,' said Mr Rusty.

'So what did you do, Mr Rusty?' said Florence.

'Oh, I've always done very well on "the circuit", I've had no problems, me,' said Mr Rusty.

Mr Rusty remembered 'the circuit' and suddenly found the magic handle rather difficult to turn with his arthritic hand . . .

'I came seventeenth in the competition for the "Pears Soap" girl,' said Florence. 'And I nearly got "Fairy Snow", but they said something about my not being "Eighties" enough!'

'Well, I did jolly well for myself,' said Ermintrude. 'I became an agony aunt with my own column in *What Cow?* magazine. The monthly for the discerning cattle enthusiast. Spin away, Mr Rusty!'

WHAT COW? 53

Dear Ermintrude

Dear Readers,
Once again it's a big thank-you kiss from Auntie Ermi for all your lovely letters. A problem aired is a problem shared, I always say, and I must say I'm feeling a lot better about myself as a result. I really was about ready to throw in the towel if it hadn't been for your lovely supportive words. Special thanks to Mrs Evans from Colchester . . .

Dear Ermintrude,

My life really hasn't been worth living for the past two years. Or so I thought. But reading your column has really put things into perspective. You really have got problems – and I don't just mean that you're a bit lumpy . . .

Yours gratefully,
D. Evans

'I got a job as entertainments manager on the pier at Blackpool,' said Brian. 'Booked all the greats in my time, I have. Mud, Showaddywaddy! – They had a name for me in the business – used to call me . . . "Mr Sunshine", that was it!'

'If you're ever reincarnated,' said Dougal, 'will you promise me you won't be a snail?'

'If you'll promise me you won't be a cheeky monkey!' said Brian, circling Dougal waggishly.

'All I can remember,' said Dylan, 'is that I, like, found this piece of paper in the Seventies with the letters "p.t.o" written on it, so I like, turned it over and, like, "p.t.o" was written on the other side too, and then it was, like, 1992 when someone took it out of my hands.'

'So what did you do in the Eighties, Dougal?' said Florence.

'Oh, corporate business mostly, you know, and the occasional book.'

'Oh, really?' said Florence.

'Yes *The Art of Business Diplomacy* by Dougal,' said Dougal.

'That sounds very interesting,' said Florence.

'Yes, over the years I've found that I have a particular gift with people. The ability to win friends and influence them, and say exactly the right thing at the right time, you know. So I thought I'd put it all down on paper so that others may learn.'

'Good idea,' said Mr McHenry, nodding wildly.

'I shall be signing copies later,' said Dougal, as Mr Rusty summoned up an extract from Dougal's book . . .

Chapter Two

If It Ain't Working – Eat Sugar

. . . and so it was that I entered into negotiations on the best way to realize the assets of the Magic Garden. The site had excellent office space development potential, if I could overcome a few minor objections from residents; namely a few birds, a snail, the more vociferous trees, a talking bread-bin, and a sitting tenant by the name of Mr Rusty.

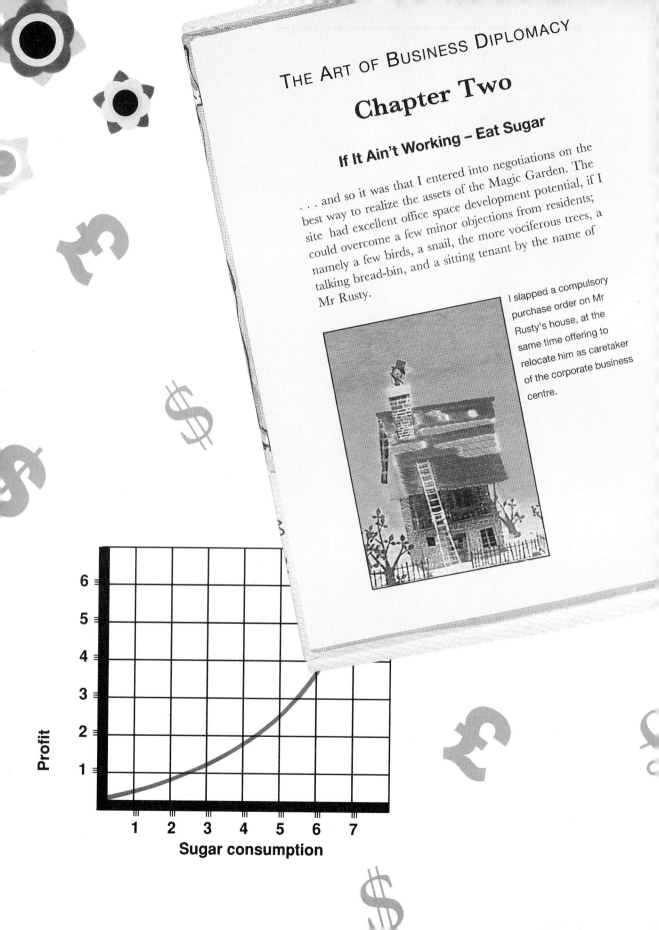

I slapped a compulsory purchase order on Mr Rusty's house, at the same time offering to relocate him as caretaker of the corporate business centre.

...xplained to the birds that under the new scheme of things there ...ould be little call for birdsong but they would each be offered a place ...n the Adult Bird Retraining Scheme where they would learn to sound ...ike something else, i.e. kettles, alarm clocks, xerox machines, etc.

The suggested repossession of shells brought the snail population into line. All remaining flora and fauna were gainfully employed as casual labour on various projects: drilling for oil, the digging of ink-wells and essential work such as the maintenance of the new sugar plantations.

'Oh, Dougal!' said Florence, when everything was back to normal. 'How awful, you ruined the garden!'

'No I didn't!' denied Dougal.

'Only because interest rates went through the roof, the city went bust and you couldn't get the investment,' said Mr McHenry.

'That's quite enough of that,' said Dougal, who was beginning to feel rather uncomfortable. 'You know, I'm suddenly feeling rather tired. Isn't it time for bed yet, Zebedee?'

'Bedtime is whenever you want it to be,' said Zebedee who had gone a bit Zen.

Florence thought she must be hearing things.

'Bedtime? Whenever you want it to be?' she said. 'Bedtime's when you say it is, Zebedee, at a particular time!'

'It is and it isn't,' said Zebedee mysteriously. 'When you achieve "The Incredible Lightness of Boing".'

'The incredible lightness of what?' said Dougal.

'It's a three-part therapy workshop retreat in healing and spiritual growth, combining shiitsu, aromatherapy and origami!' said Zebedee.

'Hey, it sounds like it could be far out,' said Dylan.

'I had to do something when the Roundabout came to a halt,' said Zebedee. 'I thought about setting up a "Jack-in-the-Box" shop in Covent Garden, but did something else instead. Shall I tell you about it?'

'Go ahead,' said Mr Rusty, who was getting pretty fed up with turning the magic handle and was glad of the break.

THE INCREDIBLE LIGHTNESS OF BOING

Zebedee cleared his throat, jumped a bit, and disappeared a few times just to get everyone's attention.

'Now the key to the "Incredible Lightness of Boing" is to understand the concept of Bedtime. Now Bedtime, like Greenwich Mean Time has its own meridian which is determined by exactly what point in time people go to bed each day – which can be any time.'

 Greenwich bedtime

'Now to achieve the "Incredible Lightness of Boing" you don't want to go to bed at a particular time, because a particular time is very particular about what you do in it and probably won't let you read a book or finish your cocoa!

'So it's a better idea to go to bed at about eightish or ninish, or sevenish or tenish, or half-past fivish or whenever you like,' said Zebedee jumping about wakefully.

'Half-past seven in the morning might not seem like the right time to go to bed; but there again what's wrong with it? It might be one of your favourite times. I'm very fond of seventeen minutes past twelve but it probably does nothing for you. And I wouldn't give half-past four the time of day.'

'Now, if you're enjoying yourself time flies, and if you're not it can drag on for ever. That's why twelve hours of daylight in the Magic Garden only lasts five minutes.

'Some days in the Magic Garden are so interesting that twelve hours go by in no time at all.'

And Zebedee summoned up the most interesting episode of *The Magic Roundabout* ever.

Da   -   da   -   da   -   da

FLORENCE: Hello, Zebedee.

ZEBEDEE: Hello, Florence, time for bed!

da   -   da   -   da   -   da

'If you are speaking to somebody incredibly boring, a five-minute conversation can last up to twenty years. I accidentally caught a speech by John Major the other day and grew an incredibly long grey beard,' continued Zebedee. 'Fortunately I was able to read an extremely interesting book and I am now only two days old. Now if you can understand all this then you are well on your way to achieving the "Incredible Lightness of Boing". You will be able to leap great distances in space and time and no child will ever question your authority. Furthermore, you qualify to go on my five-day, New-Age, creative workshop retreat. Three hundred pounds per day, two thousand pounds if you lose your concentration,' said Zebedee. 'Anyone interested?'

'Wow,' said Dylan, who quite liked the sound of it but wasn't sure he could afford to be New Age.

'Sounds like existentialism, except more expensive, to me,' said Mr Rusty.

'The trouble with enlightenment is there's always a bill at the end of it,' said Ermintrude.

Everyone sighed in agreement.

DOUGAL'S FAMILY TREE

Little evidence remains of the amazing exploits of Dougal's ancestors. The pedigrees have long since disappeared and most of the family portraits have been mysteriously destroyed. As Dougal reminds us, a family as influential as the 'Dugalles' has many detractors. We rely therefore on the scant and vague recollections of Dougal himself and the tales of heroism told on his grandmother's knee of this long and noble family.

A breed of dogs 'both fierce and frightful' alighted with William the Conqueror and are said to have terrorized King Harold's men at the Battle of Hastings.

Strangely enough, some 'foul fnarling brutes' seem to have been fighting for the English at the same time. Both the French 'Dugalles' and the English 'Dougals' record a victory, suggesting possibly that some kind of deal was struck.

The Dougals, next emerge as a proud Scottish clan, led most notably by one 'Dougal the Great', sometimes known as 'Dougal the Furry', who defended the Highlands from English invasion, and was lauded in particular by Robert the Bruce.

McDougal the Great 'A right winsome whelp'

Dougal the Great seems also to have fought on one or two crusades with the English, where a meeting with Richard the Lion Heart occasioned his almost miraculous conversion to English nationalism. He seems to have impressed Richard as a 'noble and fiery beaft' and overcome reservations about his canine origins to such an extent that he was awarded several dukedoms, so beginning the 'DuGalles" long association with royalty.

As Dougal recounts it, Dougal the Great went on to fight valiantly in the War of the Roses, and was eventually decorated by Henry VIII with his own coat of arms. Robbie Burns paid tribute to this canine chieftain in his poem beginning: 'Wee sleakin', cowerin', furry beastie'.

To have witnessed all these events however, Dougal the Great's life must have spanned at least 400 years, so he was indeed an exceptional dog, as Dougal reminds us.

No less extraordinary were the life and times of 'Dougallion', who overcame some vicious rumours about Sir Walter Raleigh and a puddle, to become the favourite of Elizabeth I. A dazzling swordsman, and ardent royalist, Dougallion was Dumas' model for *The Three Musketeers*. Dumas apparently felt his public wouldn't accept Dougallion as his sole protagonist.

'Dougallion, The Laughing Cavalier'. Franz Hals was certainly in a lighthearted mood when he painted his portrait because he signed it 'Bill Evans'.

Dougal's own lineage can be traced back directly to a liaison between Dougallion and one of King Charles II's spaniels. For this to have been possible, Dougallion must have been an incredible 303 when the pairing took place.

Dougal appears to become lost in the mists of time when questioned further, touching only fleetingly on dates and individuals from his long lineage. Suffice to say, Napoleon, Marie Curie, the Scarlet Pimpernel and several tsars of Russia are mentioned, as well as another romantic liaison between an unnamed Italian opera star and the Hound of the Baskervilles (as the latter was previously believed to be a fictional character, this casts a new light on the work of Conan Doyle).

HALLO!

AT HOME WITH 'MR. SUNSHINE'
BRIAN THE SNAIL

Brian is quiet and sensitive, and is happiest when pottering about at home. 'It takes a lot to bring me out of my shell,' he says modestly.

Best known for his role in *The Magic Roundabout*, Brian leads an international lifestyle as a professional celebrity, talent-show host and variety agent. He also finds the time to run his own international sportswear business.

Now that you're so famous and rich, don't you ever feel the need to branch out, into a bigger shell?

Brian: I grew up in this shell, and I can't imagine changing it now. I've sort of grown into it. When I'm not jet-setting across the world leading an incredibly glamorous and exciting life, I'm just plain ole me, pottering about at home. I'm a bit of a home bod really.

So being internationally famous and successful hasn't changed you?

Brian: I think deep down, I'm a rather shy sensitive person. I like nothing better than staying in, popping in and out, doing little odd jobs about the place. Being a bit of a DIY fanatic I've been able to get it just how I want it. It's amazing what you can do with one room, to make it feel more spacious.

There seems to be a certain Spanish Gold influence in the décor?

Brian: I've always loved to travel, there's a bit of a gypsy in me, always on the move – and that's how I see this place really, a roving Spanish caravan. I'm a sort of a theme snail. *Viva España!*

Your relationship with Dougal hasn't always been smooth, how are you getting along these days?

Brian: Dougal and I are really

great friends these days. In some ways I think we always were. There's virtually nothing he wouldn't share with me – all his secrets. Only the other day he told me he had massive gambling debts. He's very open, very warm – a romantic, desperate sort of a person.'

Would you prefer not to talk about the recent libel action you brought against him?

Brian: Yes. It was a very traumatic time for me. For both of us. But it's all in the past now. I think Dougal regrets calling me 'a species of pond vermin'. It's technically inaccurate, anyway. But I prefer not to talk about it – especially the fact that I won. I don't see any point gloating, do you?

You've been seen publicly with Ermintrude quite recently. Is there anyone special in your life?

Brian: Ermi is a very dear friend, we're very close. But we're both very busy at the moment as well. So when we have some spare time it's nice to do things together. That's all there is to it. We both love Tammy Wynette and enjoy going to DIY centres to buy rawl plugs or a new sink plunger. We've a lot in common.

So, Brian, do you have any regrets in your life?

Brian: I've never been one to dwell on the past, what's done is done, and I've seen a lot of water pass under the bridge. Life is a richly woven macrami wall-hanging, which we traverse as best we can. Sometimes the going's smooth and sometimes we come across funny knobbly bits with wooden beads in them. That's the way I see it anyway. **H**

Exclusive pictures of Brian's luxurious home

THE MAGIC ROUNDABOUT RETURNS

'That's almost the whole story, Florence,' said Mr Rusty, resting his hand on the Magic Roundabout. 'I would have continued on the circuit, Zebedee would have kept his therapy workshop, Dougal his property business, if something magical hadn't happened once again.'

Channel Four wanted to put *The Magic Roundabout* back on breakfast TV, and so Zebedee gathered everyone together in the garden for an early morning meeting . . .

DOUGAL: You can't tell children to go to bed at eight-thirty in the morning! They'll have just got up, have four minutes of daylight and then it'll be straight back to bed!

ZEBEDEE: Yes, but we're not exactly in the strongest of negotiating positions.

MR RUSTY: And how are they going to get the Roundabout working again, that's what I'd like to know . . . ?

Everyone was a little anxious. They hadn't seen each other for years and they certainly weren't used to breakfast meetings.

ZEBEDEE: New technology, Mr Rusty. They're going to give it a complete overhaul – even going to install a catalytic converter so it can run on lead-free petrol.

MR RUSTY: But the Roundabout doesn't run on petrol!

ZEBEDEE: It will now. They've got to find something to do with all that lead-free petrol, there is gallons of the stuff floating around.

MR McHENRY: And what about the elderflower wine to oil the magic parts? Nobody makes that nowadays.

BRIAN: Nobody is that daft any more.

ZEBEDEE: Apparently the Planer brothers still make it . . .

DOUGAL: Oh no, 'the Brothers Grim!'

Dougal ran round in a circle and then hid behind a tree.

ZEBEDEE: Channel Four say they like the whole 'garden' idea! and they're willing to 'run with it' so long as we're 'conscious of the environment' and 'ozone friendly'.

DOUGAL: And when have I not been conscious of the environment and ozone friendly?

Dougal was tempting fate asking a question like that, but luckily for him they were already in a flash-back.

FLORENCE: What does 'being conscious of the environment' mean?

MR RUSTY: Ah! Good question.

Mr Rusty thought about it for a while, as the others offered their suggestions.

TRAIN: Well for a start, people will start using me a bit more often. And about time too.

DYLAN: The environment, is, like, everything, right? It's, like, all round us, I just don't understand what 'being conscious' means.

ERMINTRUDE: The environment is all the hills and the trees and all the green bits. And all the lovely little flowers and leaves and things.

DOUGAL: It's everything that's not already lining Ermintrude's stomach.

BRIAN It's all to do with nature, and how each animal, however small, plays its part for the good of all. Otherwise we upset the ecological balance, eh, Dougal?

Dougal looked at Brian and thought it might well be worth upsetting the ecological balance, just once.

ZEBEDEE: So being conscious of the environment means knowing what's around you, not littering the garden, and collecting all your milk-bottle tops into a jar labelled 'for the planet'.

FLORENCE: I see, and what does 'ozone friendly' mean?

DYLAN: It means we've gotta, like, be friendly to ozones.

Dylan's brain was being unusually active for the time of the morning.

FLORENCE: Oh, and what are they?

DYLAN: Ozones are, like, this protected species, right, and there are, like, hardly any ozones left because hunters keep, like, killing them for their fur, and they, like, live in Peru in a rain forest and we've gotta, like 'save the ozone' or they'll become extinct, right?

ERMINTRUDE: Poor little ozones! Perhaps we should adopt one?

DOUGAL: Why not! We've got every other conceivable animal on the programme, why not have a dear little ozone? I'm sure it's more advanced in its evolution than a snail!

ZEBEDEE: I'm not sure that's what they meant about our being aware of the environment! Maybe we all have to become ecologists . . .

BRIAN: You mean like that sports commentator chap . . .

DOUGAL: I certainly hope not.

DYLAN: Hey, I hear sweet music!

Unaccustomed mental exertion had tipped Donovan's song 'Catch the wind' into Dylan's conscious mind and he was enjoying it for the first time. Zebedee looked around at the others, saw that nothing had changed and decided the meeting was over, the motion passed, and that it was time for lunch.

'And that, Florence, is the story of how we got to be here,' said Mr Rusty, conclusively, patting the new Roundabout.

'Is it all crystal clear to you now?' said Brian.

'Well, sort of,' said Florence, who didn't look at all sure.

'Anything you want to ask, just go right ahead,' said Mr Rusty, generously.

Florence scratched her head and thought about France and the Roundabout, the cross-Channel ferry, the BBC, Ermintrude, Dougal's Hollywood cocktail and the ozones, and then she thought about her question and she wasn't quite sure whether anyone had answered it, so she asked it again.

'Yes, but how did we get to be here?' said Florence.

Zebedee and Mr Rusty and all the animals sighed because Florence's child-like naïvety could be a little exasperating at times. Then everyone went rather quiet. Thumbs were twiddled, by those that had them, moustaches were twitched, hoofs were tapped, paws shuffled. Some looked up at the clouds and hummed, others wriggled about a bit, until at last the silence was broken.

'Time for bed,' said Zebedee.

And they all agreed, so it must have been bedtime. And Florence's question would just have to wait for another lovely day in the Magic Garden.